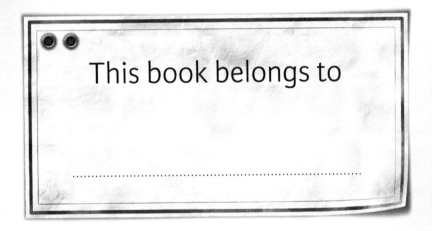

This book belongs to

....

LIZARD LOU

a collection of rhymes old and new

Copyright © 2011 by All About Learning Press, Inc.
Printed in the United States of America

All About Learning Press, Inc.
2038 E. Anvil Lake Road
Eagle River, WI 54521

ISBN 978-1-935197-15-7

Cover Design: David LaTulippe
Page Layout: Renée LaTulippe
Illustrations: Donna Goeddaeus

Lizard Lou: a collection of rhymes old and new is part of the *All About Reading* program. For more books in this series, go to www.AllAboutReading.com.

To the reader –

buzz like a bee
from rhyme to rhyme
and read them aloud
one at a time

Megan Has a Spoon

Megan has a spoon,
Megan has a pot,
Megan has some cinnamon
and likes to bake a lot.

Megan has some apples,
Megan has some dough,
Megan puts them in a tin
and fixes them just so.

Megan adds some sugar
and a little nutmeg too.
What does Megan bake all day?
An apple pie for you!

—*Renée LaTulippe*

Animal Crackers

Animal crackers and cocoa to drink,
that is the finest of suppers, I think.

When I'm grown up and can have what I please,
I think I shall always insist upon these.

What do YOU choose when you're offered a treat?
When Mother says, "What would you like best to eat?"
Is it waffles and syrup, or cinnamon toast?
It's cocoa and animals that I love most!

The kitchen's the coziest place that I know;
the kettle is singing, the stove is aglow,
and there in the twilight, how jolly to see
the cocoa and animals waiting for me.

—*Christopher Morley*

The Ant Explorer

Once a little sugar ant made up his mind to roam—
to go away, far away, far away from home.
He had eaten all his breakfast, and he had his ma's consent
to see what he should chance to see,
and here's the way he went:
Up and down a fern plant, round and round a stone,
down a gloomy gully where he feared to be alone,
up a mighty mountain range, seven inches high,
through the fearful forest grass that nearly hid the sky,
out along a bracken bridge, bending in the moss,
till he reached a dreadful desert, feet and feet across.

'Twas a dry, deserted desert, and a trackless land to tread;
he wished that he was home again
and tucked up tight in bed.

His little legs were wobbly, his strength was nearly spent,
and so he turned around again,
and here's the way he went:
Back away from desert lands, feet and feet across,
back along the bracken bridge bending in the moss,
through the fearful forest grass shutting out the sky,
up a mighty mountain range, seven inches high,
down a gloomy gully where he feared to be alone,
up and down a fern plant and round and round a stone.

A dreary ant, a weary ant, resolved no more to roam—
he staggered up the garden path and popped back home.

—*C. J. Dennis*

A Bird Came Down the Walk

A bird came down the walk:
he did not know I saw.
He bit an angle-worm in halves
and ate the fellow, raw.

And then he drank a dew
from a convenient grass,
and then hopped sidewise to the wall
to let a beetle pass.

—*Emily Dickinson*

Davey Roy

Davey Roy,
little boy,
clever, smart, and wise—
on the stair
(not in a chair)
sits and bats his eyes.
Halfway up
and halfway down—
in the middle, say.
He's just a lad
who's simply glad
to sit and think all day.

—*Renée LaTulippe*

Bat, Bat, Come Under My Hat

Bat, bat, come under my hat,
and I'll give you a slice of bacon.
And when I bake,
I'll give you a cake,
if I am not mistaken.

—*traditional English rhyme*

The Gift

A crow flew down one wintry eve
and sat upon my sill.
He had a pinecone in his claw
and a sleigh bell in his bill.

He looked at me, I looked at him,
he shook his little head,
as if to play a tune for me
before I went to bed.

He tapped the pinecone on the sill
to free a nut or two,
invited me to dine with him,
then up and away he flew.

His silver bell tinkled a sweet goodbye
as he rose so sure and swift.
He'd just come down to say hello
and leave his simple gift.

—Renée LaTulippe

The Purple Cow

I never saw a purple cow;
I never hope to see one.
But I can tell you anyhow,
I'd rather see than be one!

—*Gelett Burgess*

Coward Crocodile

My snout is long,
my teeth are sharp,
my bite is hard and strong.
But when I see
a slimy eel,
I squeal and scream "So long!"

I run with speed,
my claws can scratch,
my tail can crush a stone.
So why do I
cry in the dark
when I am left alone?

I don't like bugs
or snakes or storms,
nor my cousins in the Nile!
Sometimes I even
scare myself—
I'm just a coward crocodile.

—Renée LaTulippe

A Little Deer Played in the Wood

A little deer played in the wood
  beside the bubbling creek.
As I came near, she simply stood
  and let me brush her cheek.

Such eyes I'd never seen before,
  so deeply brown and sweet.
She blinked and hopped away once more
  on dainty little feet.

—*Renée LaTulippe*

The Little Donkey

I saw a donkey
one day old,
his head was too big
for his neck to hold.
His legs were shaky
and long and loose,
they rocked and staggered
and weren't much use.
His queer little coat
was soft and grey,
and curled at his neck
in a lovely way.
He tried to gambol
and frisk a bit,
but he wasn't sure
of the trick of it.

His face was wistful,
and left no doubt
that he felt life needed
some thinking out.
So he blundered round
in venturous quest,
and then lay flat
on the ground to rest.
He looked so little
and weak and slim,
I prayed the world
might be good to him.

—*traditional Irish rhyme*

The Dandelion

Oh, dandelion, yellow as gold,
what do you do all day?

I just wait here in the tall green grass
till the children come to play.

Oh, dandelion, yellow as gold,
what do you do all night?

I wait and wait till the cool dews fall
and my hair grows long and white.

And what do you do when your hair is white,
and the children come to play?

They take me up in their dimpled hands
and blow my hair away.

—*Unknown*

Only My Echo

Up on the hilltop,
I yell to the sea,
but only my echo
comes back to me.

Up on the hilltop,
I sing out with glee,
but only my echo
comes back to me.

Up to the hilltop
I often flee
to listen for my echo
coming back to me.

To listen for my echo
coming back to me.

—*Renée LaTulippe*

An Elephant Walks Like This

An elephant walks like this and that.
He's terribly tall and terribly fat.
He has no fingers, he has no toes,
but goodness gracious, what a nose!

—*traditional English rhyme*

Did You Ever Hear?

Did you ever hear of the elk who lays eggs
high in the top of a tree?
Or the short giraffe who flew an aircraft
across the Caribbean Sea?

Did you ever hear of the donkey Pierre
who works as a lumberjack?
Or the green-eyed goat with the goofy grin
who likes to bake cakes for a snack?

Well, I'm here to tell you that I've seen them all,
and they're really quite strange, I admit.
But these things exist as sure as I'm here—
I wouldn't mislead you a bit.

Did you ever hear of the spotted sloth
who zips around on a motorbike?
Or the snake who plays the accordion
for weasels and monkeys alike?

Well, I'm here to tell you that I've seen them all
and they're really quite odd, I admit.
And if I were you, I'd keep my eyes peeled—
and I wouldn't believe me a bit!

—*Renée LaTulippe*

Firefly

Hey, little firefly,
why so shy?
Your flickering light
is a star in the sky.

Hey, little firefly,
hold your head high.
Your tiny lantern
is a diamond in my eye.

Hey, little firefly,
the night slipped by.
Please light my way home
before we say goodbye.

—*Renée LaTulippe*

One, Two, Three, Four, Five

One, two, three, four, five,
once I caught a fish alive.
Six, seven, eight, nine, ten,
then I let it go again.

Why did you let it go?
Because it bit my finger so.

Which finger did it bite?
The little one upon the right.

—traditional English rhyme

If I Had a Wheel

If I had a wheel,
I'd roll it into town,
or maybe I could even
wear it like a crown.
I'd throw it like a Frisbee
or spin it like a hoop,
or use it as a feeder
inside the chicken coop.
I'd fill it up with dirt
and plant some flowers there,
or bend it in the middle
and make a rubber chair.
I could float it down the river
or hang it in a tree,
and swing high in the air
where no one could catch me.

—Renée LaTulippe

I'd Like to Have a Little Yard

I'd like to have a little yard,
something very small,
just big enough to put a horse
and a cozy little stall.

I'd get a goat to put inside
to keep him company,
and they could neigh and bleat all day
in perfect harmony.

We'd need a goose to put in there,
a bunny rabbit, too.
And maybe just one other thing...
a thing that might say "Moo."

With all of us together there,
I think we'd have a ball...
perhaps that little yard I'd like
won't be so small at all.

—*Renée LaTulippe*

The Gardener

I weed my garden every morn
till every single weed is gone,

for when the weeds are gone, I know,
the flowers will much prettier grow.

But many of the weeds I throw away
are just as pretty, I must say,

and love the sun and pleasant showers
as much, I'm sure, as do the flowers.

So I am sorry when I pull
the weeds: it seems unmerciful.

And often, weeding in my garden,
I say, "Excuse me" and "Beg pardon."

—*Ralph Bergengren*

Sour Sweetie

Sweetie was a little girl
who lived deep in a wood.
She never learned her manners, though,
like every child should.

She put her feet upon the table
and ate with her mouth wide.
And if you told her to be good,
she'd cross her arms and "Humph!" with pride.

If there were cookies to be had,
she ate them all herself,
and woe to anyone at all
who sought them on the shelf.

Although her name was sugar sweet,
her face was always grim.
She never laughed or danced or played—
she kept the lights down dim.

All who knew her tried in vain
to make her nice (and not so greedy).
But she just snapped and called them names—
And now they call her Sour Sweetie.

—*Renée LaTulippe*

The Wind

The wind came a-whooping down Cranberry Hill
and stole an umbrella from Mother Medill.
It picked up a paper on Patterson's Place
and carried it clean to the Rockaby Race.
And what was more shocking and awful than that,
it blew the new feather off grandmother's hat.

—*Leroy F. Jackson*

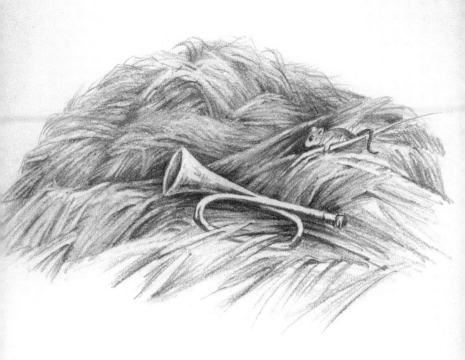

Little Boy Blue

Little Boy Blue, come blow your horn.
The sheep's in the meadow,
the cow's in the corn.

Where is the boy
who looks after the sheep?
He's under a haystack, fast asleep.

—*traditional English rhyme*

I Wanted a Harp

I wanted a harp with golden strings
and a dog without the fleas.
A sheep, a feast, three butterfly wings,
and a nose that doesn't sneeze.

I wanted a house built into a hill
and a crate of exotic teas.
A fish, a pig, a porcupine quill,
and a goose that I could squeeze.

I wanted a horse as brave as a knight
and a garden full of peas.
A kite, a bike, a bird in flight,
and a thousand cherry trees.

I wanted a hound dog raised by a king
and a simple life of ease.
But I never got a single thing—
perhaps I should have said *please*.

—*Renée LaTulippe*

The Itch

I had an itch I couldn't reach,
I really had to itch it.
I hopped and skipped and jumped around—
anything to scritch it!

I tried to figure out just where
the itch was itching most,
so I could scratch that little spot
against the hitching post.

The itch was where no post could go;
I had to twist and twitch.
I went all sideways upside-down
to get that little itch.

It seemed that itch would last all day,
no hope had I to ditch it.
But then I saw my shirt was wool—
so I just had to switch it.

—*Renée LaTulippe*

Going to Alaska

Scotty's an adventurer;
he's traveled far and wide.
Now he's gone off to Alaska
with his puppy by his side.

He went to see the glaciers
and slid along the ice,
then camped inside an igloo
and ate caribou with rice.

He looked for tufted puffins
and bought some fishing bait,
then threw a rock with all his might
across the Bering Strait.

He snowshoed through the Klondike—
ten cold and snowy nights!—
then hiked to Eagle River
to see the Northern Lights.

Yes, Scotty's an adventurer;
he's traveled far and wide.
Now he's gone off to Alaska
with his puppy by his side.

—Renée LaTulippe

The Triantiwontigongolope

There's a very funny insect that you do not often spy,
and it isn't quite a spider and it isn't quite a fly.
It is something like a beetle, and a little like a bee,
but nothing like a woolly grub that climbs upon a tree.
Its name is quite a hard one, but you'll learn it soon, I hope.
So try: *Tri- Tri-anti-wonti-* **Triantiwontigongolope.**

It lives on weeds and wattle-gum, and has a funny face.
Its appetite is hearty, and its manners a disgrace.
When first you come upon it, it will give you quite a scare,
but when you look for it again, you find it isn't there.
And unless you call it softly, it will stay away and mope.
So try: *Tri- Tri-anti-wonti-* **Triantiwontigongolope.**

It trembles if you tickle it, or tread upon its toes.
It is not an early riser, but it has a snubbish nose.
If you sneer at it, or scold it, it will scuffle off in shame,
but it purrs and purrs quite proudly if you call it by its name,
and offer it some sandwiches of sealing-wax and soap.
So try: *Tri- Tri-anti-wonti-* **Triantiwontigongolope.**

But of course you haven't seen it, and I truthfully confess,
that I haven't see it either, and I don't know its address.
For there isn't such an insect,
though there really might have been,
if the trees and grass were purple,
and the sky was bottle green.
It's just a little joke of mine, which you'll forgive, I hope.
So try: *Tri- Tri-anti-wonti-*
Triantiwontigongolope.

—*C. J. Dennis*

42

Julie Jay

Julie Jay was in a jam;
she really couldn't beat it—
she fell into a jelly jar
without a spoon to eat it.

With jelly here and jelly there,
it was a sticky climb.
But Julie Jay just licked her lips
and took her own sweet time.

—*Renée LaTulippe*

Snowflakes

The snowflakes are falling by ones and by twos;
there's snow on my jacket, and snow on my shoes.
There's snow on the bushes, and snow on the trees;
it's snowing on everything now, if you please.

—*Leroy F. Jackson*

Critters

His twisty ways and beady eyes
that glitter like two jewels
might make the snake a thing despised—
but I think he's pretty cool.

And what about the kindly snail,
so often called a pest?
If there were room inside his shell,
I'd gladly be his guest.

Let's not forget our friends with legs,
the kind with six or eight.
Beetles, spiders, tiny bugs—
I think they're sort of great.

Snakes and snails and little bugs
might give some folks the jitters.
But if I could, I'd give 'em hugs,
for I like those creepy critters.

—Renée LaTulippe

The Clockwork Doll

I have a lovely clockwork doll
that winds up with a key.
And when she's wound, she walks along
as steady as can be.

The other toys all envy her
and watch her as she goes.
They wish that they had winding keys
and dainty clockwork toes.

One fault she has—she walks too fast,
and though I shout "Take care!"
She spills her eggs and knocks her head
against the nursery chair.

—traditional English rhyme

Summer Afternoon

There is nothing better
than a summer afternoon,
flying kites of many colors—
purple, blue, maroon.

Mine is orange and yellow
and shaped like a butterfly.
I love to watch it soar and dive,
then climb back to the sky.

Its rainbow-colored tail
dances up so gracefully...

Oh, wait! I think it's stuck
in that giant willow tree!

It's tangled in the branches
and I cannot shake it loose.
My lovely yellow butterfly
looks like a tattered moose!

Well!
There is nothing worse
than a summer afternoon,
losing kites up in the trees—
I think I'll just go home.

—Renée LaTulippe

Two Little Kittens, One Stormy Night

Two little kittens, one stormy night,
began to quarrel and then to fight.
One had a mouse and the other had none,
and that's the way the quarrel begun.

"I'll have that mouse," said the biggest cat.
"You'll have that mouse? We'll see about that!"
"I will have that mouse," said the eldest son.
"You shan't have that mouse," said the little one.

I told you before 'twas a stormy night
when these two little kittens began to fight.
The old woman seized her sweeping broom
and swept the two kittens right out of the room.

The ground was covered with frost and snow,
and the two little kittens had nowhere to go.
So they laid down on the mat at the door
while the old woman finished sweeping the floor.

Then they crept in, as quiet as mice,
all wet with snow and as cold as ice,
for they found it was better, that stormy night,
to lie down and sleep than to quarrel and fight.

—*traditional English rhyme*

Terrible Tim

Haven't you heard of Terrible Tim?
Well, don't you get in the way of him!
He eats lions for breakfast
and leopards for lunch,
and gobbles them down
with one terrible crunch.
He could mix a whole city
all up in a mess.
He could drink up a sea
or an ocean, I guess.
You'd better be watching for Terrible Tim,
and run when you first get your peepers on him.

—*Leroy F. Jackson*

Lizard Lou

Lizard Lou looked back one day
as he lazed on a rock in the sun.
His happy face turned to dismay—
where his tail should be, was none!

"I lost my tail—oh no, oh no!
My lizard life is done!"
He should not have fretted so,
'cuz soon, he grew a new one.

—*Renée LaTulippe*

Lollipop Gone

One lick, two licks, three licks, four.
I have a lollipop—who could want more?
Five licks, six licks, seven licks, eight.
It's getting smaller, but I can't wait!
Nine licks, ten licks, eleven licks, stop!
I can barely see my lollipop.
Twelve licks, thirteen... I'm feeling sick.
Fourteen, fifteen—
and now it's just a stick!

—Renée LaTulippe

When the Moon Is There

When the moon is there,
at half past six tonight,
we'll sit out in the garden
to watch the fading light.

And when the moon is there,
we'll have a bite to eat;
a slice of bread, a glass of milk,
and maybe something sweet.

And when the moon is there,
when it looks so small and far,
we'll gather at the window
to name the brightest star.

You'll stare up to the heavens,
your eyes so round and bright—
and when the moon is *there*,
I'll kiss you all goodnight.

—*Renée LaTulippe*

Little Mouse

I have seen you, little mouse,
running all about the house.
Through the hole, I see your eye
in the baseboard peeping sly,
hoping for some crumbs to steal
to make yourself a hearty meal.

Look before you venture out—
see if kitty is about.
If she's gone, you'll quickly run
to the kitchen for some fun.
Round about the dishes creep,
taking into each a peep
to choose a tasty tidbit there—
for you, it is a generous fare.

—*traditional English rhyme*

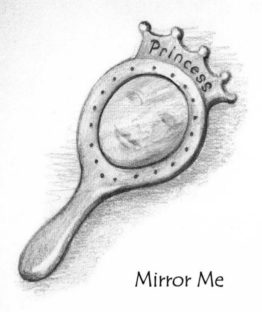

Mirror Me

I saw a girl about my age
who smiled, waved, and winked.
She copied every move I made,
and when I blinked, she blinked.

She wore the clothes I always wore,
had ribbons in her hair.
And when I turned away from her,
she was no longer there.

I thought we'd be the best of friends,
but it was not to be—
for sadly, I discovered that
she's just my mirror me.

—Renée LaTulippe

Two Lonely Birds

Our little bird sings just one song.
She warbles and coos all day long.
Hulla-loo-loo, hulla-loo, hulla-loo.
What's a lonely bird to do?

She looks in a mirror—what does she see?
Just a single little bird in a sad old tree.
Hulla-loo-loo, hulla-loo, hulla-loo.
What's a lonely bird to do?

In flies another bird who settles in the nest.
What will he do, this unexpected guest?
Hulla-loo-loo, hulla-loo, hulla-loo.
What's a lonely bird to do?

Two little birds singing just one song,
warbling and cooing all day long.
Hulla-loo-loo, hulla-loo, hulla-loo.
Two lonely birds who don't know what to do.

—*Renée LaTulippe*

I Had a Little Nut Tree

I had a little nut tree,
nothing would it bear
but a silver nutmeg
and a golden pear.
The King of Spain's daughter
came to visit me,
all for the sake
of my little nut tree.
I skipped over water,
I danced over sea,
and all the birds in the air
couldn't catch me.

—*traditional English rhyme*

A Little Newt

If you find a little newt
snacking on a garden root,
sweetly offer him a fruit...
or he'll think you have bad manners.

If you find a little newt
hiding in your laundry chute,
kindly dress him in a suit...
or he'll think you have bad manners.

If you find a little newt
sitting on your silver flute,
show him how to make it toot...
or he'll think you have bad manners.

If you find a little newt
trembling underneath your boot,
gently ask him *please do scoot*...
or he'll think you have bad manners.

If you find a little newt
grinning, small, and mostly mute,
tell him that he's terribly cute!
And he'll thank you for your manners.

—*Renée LaTulippe*

Tiny Tina Tinseltooth

It happened one October,
when the leaves had turned to gold,
and Tiny Tina Tinseltooth
had got a nasty cold.

She wobbled to the kitchen sink
to fill a water bottle—
the only problem was, poor thing,
she turned it on full throttle.

That water came a-pourin' down
and overflowed the bowl.
No matter what she did, that flood
would not go down the hole.

The kitchen turned into a lake
with every passing minute,
and by the time the moon was up,
there was an otter in it.

Then came fishes, frogs, and eels,
and some birds of prey,
and Tiny Tina Tinseltooth
had to move away.

—*Renée LaTulippe*

If I Were an Ocelot

If I were an ocelot,
I'd sleep the livelong day.
I'd curl up in the moss a lot
or in a bale of hay.

If I were an ocelot,
I'd dine upon the heath,
and I'd be sure to floss a lot,
so I'd never lose my teeth.

If I were an ocelot,
I'd snack on leaves and bugs.
I'd eat tomato sauce a lot
on tasty little slugs.

If I were an ocelot,
I'd get a catnip ball
that I'd be sure to toss a lot
against the garden wall.

And if I were an ocelot,
I'd never pick a fight.
I'd surely not be cross a lot,
and never, ever bite.

—Renée LaTulippe

Opposite Otto

Opposite Otto is an odd little boy
who lives in Oblong, Illinois.
He's made a name in his hometown—
for whatever he does is upside down.

He walks on his hands instead of his feet;
his sandwich is bread between slices of meat.
He lies under the mattress when he goes to bed,
keeps the ox in the house and lives in the shed.

He cries over cupcakes but eats onions raw.
When his toys get broken, he shouts, "Hurrah!"
His lights are on by day and off by night;
he thinks belching loudly is polite.

He puts his potatoes under his plate
and counts the nine before the eight.
He reads his books from end to start
and throws the dartboard at the dart.

You never know what Otto's about;
he's topsy-turvy and inside-out.
For messes and muddles, he's got a knack—
why, even his name goes forward and back!

—*Renée LaTulippe*

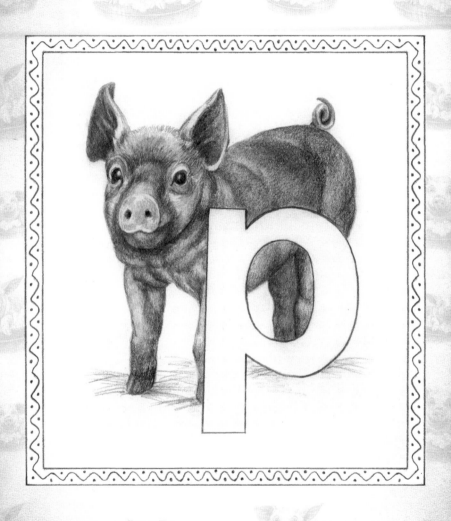

Sticky Pig

I heard a rustling in the lane,
and sounds of *smack!* and *smush!*
I pushed aside the brambles there—
my pig in the berry bush!

He'd trampled berries left and right
to make himself some jelly—
and whatever wasn't on his face
was surely in his belly.

My sticky friend came home with me
from his hideaway on the path,
and then I saw a sight so silly—
my pig in a bubble bath.

—*Renée LaTulippe*

High in the Pine Tree

High in the pine tree,
the little turtledove
made a little nursery
to please her little love.
"Coo," said the turtledove.
"Coo," said she,
in the long shady branches
of the dark pine tree.

—*traditional English rhyme*

The Policeman

I'm sure the strongest man in town
is our policeman, Mr. Brown.
One day he kindly let me feel
his muscle—it was hard as steel.

I guess he wouldn't mind to fight
with burglars in a house all night,
and then next morning, clean and neat,
you'd see him coming down the street.

He wears a uniform of blue
that always looks as good as new,
and in his pocket, the back one,
I have been told he has a gun.

But if you know him, you will find
Policeman Brown is very kind.
And when he meets you on his way,
he'll nod and pass the time of day.

That is, if you are good—if not,
he will arrest you on the spot!

—*Ralph Bergengren*

Over in the Meadow

Over in the meadow, in the sand in the sun,
lived an old mother frog and her little froggie one.
"Croak!" said the mother. "I croak," said the one.
So they croaked and were glad in the sand in the sun.

Over in the meadow, in the pond so blue,
lived an old mother duck and her little ducks two.
"Quack!" said the mother. "We quack," said the two.
So they quacked and were glad in the pond so blue.

Over in the meadow, in a hole in a tree,
lived an old mother robin and her little birds three.
"Chirp!" said the mother. "We chirp," said the three.
So they chirped and were glad in the hole in the tree.

Over in the meadow, on a rock by the shore,
lived an old mother snake and her little snakes four.
"Hiss!" said the mother. "We hiss," said the four.
So they hissed and were glad on a rock by the shore.

Over in the meadow, in a big beehive,
lived an old mother bee and her little bees five.
"Buzz!" said the mother. "We buzz," said the five.
So they buzzed and were glad in the big beehive.

—*traditional English rhyme*

The Queen of Hearts

The Queen of Hearts,
she made some tarts
all on a summer's day.

The Knave of Hearts,
he stole the tarts
and took them clean away.

The King of Hearts
called for the tarts
and gave the Knave what for.

The Knave of Hearts
brought back the tarts
and vowed he'd steal no more.

—*traditional English rhyme*

Misunderstood Mark

"Sit up straight!" they always say,
or "Stand up nice and tall!"
"What's the point," I ask myself,
"to be a question mark at all?"

For no one seems to understand,
I've been curled since my creation,
and if I straighten up too much,
I'll be an exclamation!

—*Renée LaTulippe*

The Rabbit Band

Late one night in the lettuce patch,
where scarecrows guard the land,
I heard a snazzy jazzy tune
played by a rabbit band.

One tap-tapped on a carrot,
one munch-munched on a leaf,
one snip-snipped on a turnip root,
one whistled through his teeth.

One chomp-chomped on a shallot,
one thump-thumped with his paws—
and at the end, those bunnies got
a round of loud applause.

—*Renée La Tulippe*

Under the Willow

Put down your pillow under the willow,
hang up your hat in the sun,
and lie down to snooze as long as you choose,
for the plowing and sowing are done.

Pick up your pillow from under the willow,
and clamber out into the sun.
Get a fork and a rake, for goodness' sake,
for the harvest time has begun.

—*Leroy F. Jackson*

As I Was Walking Near the Lake

As I was walking near the lake,
I met a little rattlesnake.
He ate so much jelly-cake,
it made his little belly ache.

—*traditional English rhyme*

We Saw the Shadow

A squirrel lived in our garden,
and played in sun and rain.
And though we never saw him,
we saw his shadow plain.

He made a lot of noise
with his chatter: "Chee! Chee! Chee!"
And all the nuts were stolen
from our lovely almond tree.

We tried to lure the little guy
with acorns, leaves, and flowers.
But he refused to show his face,
and left us there for hours.

We saw that shadow leap so high,
then on a branch descend.
We craned our necks and squeezed our eyes
to glimpse our timid friend.

But no matter how we turned
and no matter how we twirled,
we always saw the shadow,
but we never saw the squirrel.

—Renée LaTulippe

The Scorpion

The scorpion is as black as soot;
  he dearly loves to bite.
He is a most unpleasant brute
  to find in bed at night.

—*Hilaire Belloc*

The Snowman

One day we built a snowman,
we built him out of snow.
You should have seen how fine he was,
all white from top to toe.

We poured some water over him
to freeze his legs and ears,
and when we went indoors to bed,
we thought he'd last for years.

But in the night a warmer kind
of wind began to blow,
and Jack Frost cried and ran away,
and with him went the snow.

When we went out next morning
to bid our friend good day,
there wasn't any snowman there...
he'd melted right away!

—*traditional English rhyme*

The Little Turtle

There was a little turtle;
he lived in a box.
He swam in a puddle
and climbed on the rocks.

He snapped at a mosquito,
he snapped at a flea,
he snapped at a minnow,
and he snapped at me.

He caught the mosquito,
he caught the flea,
he caught the minnow,
but he didn't catch me!

—*Vachel Lindsay*

The Camping Trip

Down to the clearing
by our mother we were sent
to camp beside the river
in our trusty little tent.
But when the pack was opened,
all the metal poles were bent,
so we folded up our stuff again,
and trudging home we went.

—*Renée LaTulippe*

Christopher Crump

Christopher Crump,
all in a lump,
sits like a toad on the top of a stump.
He stretches and sighs
and blinks with his eyes,
bats at the beetles and fights off the flies.

—*Leroy F. Jackson*

All Kinds of Cows

The best chocolate milk is made by brown cows;
it's creamy and smooth and nutritious.
It's better than candy and makes you say "Wow!"
because it's so "udderly" delicious.

For strawberry milk, the cow must be pink—
a job that is really ambitious!
A cow must work hard to make such a drink—
and make it so "udderly" delicious.

But if you prefer a frothy milkshake,
the cow must be playful, capricious.
She must shimmy and jump and shiver and quake
to make it so "udderly" delicious.

There are all kinds of cows and all kinds of milk—
the plainest of all is just white.
But the cows named here are more precious than silk,
for their milk is an "udder" delight.

—*Renée LaTulippe*

88

Utter Nonsense

One night he showed up in our gutter,
a small strange guest with wings aflutter.
All day long he'll mope and mutter,
but his name he'll never utter.

We caught him swinging on the shutter
and pulling weeds for Mrs. Nutter.
He'll stomp around and dust the clutter,
but his name he'll never utter.

He'll sit and watch the teapot sputter,
kick the chairs and lick the butter.
His antics often make us shudder,
but his name he'll never utter.

—Renée LaTulippe

Ugly Pants

I have a pair of ugly pants
with rips around the knees—
they have pink stripes and polka-dots
and smell like moldy cheese.

They're made of fleece and burlap,
and they're weird and warm and snuggly.
If I wore them to a costume ball,
I'd win the prize for ugly.

I wear them every weekend,
though the other kids may tease,
but I just love my ugly pants
for climbing in the trees.

I know I shouldn't boast or brag,
but I can say this smugly:
no one has a pair of pants
so perfectly, beautifully ugly!

—*Renée LaTulippe*

The Vulture

The vulture eats between his meals,
and that's the reason why
he very, very rarely feels
as well as you and I.

His eye is dull, his head is bald,
his neck is growing thinner.
Oh! what a lesson for us all
to only eat at dinner!

—*Hilaire Belloc*

The Music of Your Voice

A vase upon the mantelpiece,
a ship upon the sea,
a goat upon a mountaintop
are much the same to me.
But when you mention melon jam,
or picnics by the creek,
or apple pies, or pantomimes,
I love to hear you speak.

—*C. J. Dennis*

Skipping Stones

I sometimes spend an hour or two
on the banks of Benning Brook,
choosing all the smoothest stones
from every little nook.

I put them in my pockets
and head down to Crandon Creek,
and send them skipping one by one—
like vessels, flat and sleek.

—*Renée LaTulippe*

Upon the Irish Sea

Someone told Maria Ann,
Maria Ann told me,
that kittens ride in coffee cans
upon the Irish Sea.

From quiet caves to rolling waves,
how jolly it must be
to travel in a coffee can
upon the Irish Sea!

But when it snows and when it blows,
how would *you* like to be
a kitten in a coffee can
upon the Irish Sea?

—*Leroy F. Jackson*

The Worm

When the earth is turned in spring,
the worms are fat as anything,

and birds come flying all around
to eat the worms right off the ground.

They like the worms just as much as I
like bread and milk and apple pie.

And once, when I was very young,
I put a worm right on my tongue.

I didn't like the taste a bit,
and so I didn't swallow it.

But oh, it makes my mother squirm,
because she *thinks* I ate that worm!

—*Ralph Bergengren*

Time to Rise

A birdie with a yellow bill
hopped upon my window sill,
cocked his shining eye and said:
"Ain't you 'shamed, you sleepy-head!"

—*Robert Louis Stevenson*

Kisses and Hugs

You can take a trip to Xanadu
or play the xylophone.
You can even take an X-ray
to see a broken bone.

You can put me in a little box
or tie me in a knot,
or stick me on a treasure map
where I can mark the spot.

But the best thing you can do
with a little X like me,
is write XOXO—
that's kisses and hugs, you see!

—*Renée LaTulippe*

The Axman

High on the hill, where the tall trees grow,
there lives an axman that I know.
From his little hut by a ferny creek,
day after day, week after week,

he goes each morn with his shining ax,
trudging along by the forest tracks.
And he chops and he chops till the daylight goes
high on the hill, where the blue-gum grows.

—*C. J. Dennis*

I Have Spots and Twisty Ears

I have spots and twisty ears,
a coat so thick and warm.
I run barefoot in the snow
and frolic in a storm.

I have eyes that see by night,
and a pretty face, I thinks.
I climb trees in a single pounce—
I'm a clever little lynx!

—*Renée LaTulippe*

My Kitty Had a Ball of Yarn

My kitty had a ball of yarn
that kept her really busy.
She rolled it all around the house
and made her poor self dizzy.

She rolled it through the chair legs
and around the bedroom doors.
She rolled it down the staircase
and underneath a chest of drawers.

She rolled that ball of yarn all day,
until it was no more.
By night it was a single string,
limp upon the floor.

She batted at the tail of yarn—
it didn't want to play!
She tipped her head and stared a bit,
then up and pranced away.

—*Renée LaTulippe*

Second Chance Yo-yo

I see my yellow yo-yo
lying in the heap,
the heap of toys I can't decide
to throw away or keep.

I used to spin it all day long
up and down its string.
I think it was my favorite toy,
to spin and catch and fling!

But then one day it turned on me
and whacked me in the chin.
It wrapped itself around my arms,
and I think I saw it grin!

Once I got untangled,
I flung it far away,
and there it has been lying
ever since that fateful day.

I guess I'll give it a second chance;
it used to make me smile—
but if it gets out of hand again,
it goes back on the pile!

—Renée LaTulippe

Sleepy Sean

I knew a boy who was so bored
they called him Sleepy Sean.
He ended every sentence
with a yodel and a yawn.

He sometimes played with marbles,
rode a tractor 'round the lawn,
but nothing seemed to please him—
just that yodel and a yawn.

Deciding he should see the world,
he packed and left at dawn.
The only things he left behind
were his yodel and his yawn.

It's been a decade, maybe more,
since Sean was up and gone,
but sometimes I remember him—
with a yodel and a yawn.

—*Renée LaTulippe*

Zip It

Terry had a pair of slippers
with two buttons and two zippers.

The buttons fastened well enough;
the zippers, though, were kind of tough.

He yanked and pulled and bit his lip,
but those two slippers wouldn't zip.

He took one off and tried to flip it,
pulled some more, but couldn't zip it.

Terry had a pair of clippers—
and has no more those unzipped slippers.

—*Renée La Tulippe*

Don't Feed the Seals Zucchini

Don't feed the seals zucchini
or pie with lemon zest,
or make the zebras run around
in plaid and paisley vests.

Don't strap the spider monkeys
to the roof of the family car,
or feed cupcakes and ice cream
to antelopes from Zanzibar.

Don't zigzag through the rhino cage
or make hyenas laugh,
and never play the zither
for a sensitive giraffe.

Don't tap dance with the penguins,
no matter what you do—
oh, there's so much to remember
on a visit to the zoo!

—Renée LaTulippe

Counting Sheep

Lying awake with my eyes open wide,
blanket to my chin and Teddy by my side,
waiting and hoping to drift to sleep...
maybe it'll happen if I count some sheep.

Ten sheep grazing in the meadow grass.
Nine sheep lazing as the hours pass.
Eight sheep blinking at old farmer Mel.
Seven sheep drinking at the village well.
Six sheep romping in a light summer rain.
Five sheep stomping down a country lane.

Four sheep giving their wool away.
Three sheep living by Moonlight Bay.
Two sheep wandering on a wooded path.
One sheep pondering a warm sudsy bath.

Zero sheep peeping with eyes open wide...
And one child sleeping with Teddy by his side.

Zzzzzzzz...

—Renée LaTulippe

Index of Poems